CONTENTS

WHO'S WHO

Oprah Winfrey
Oprah is the undisputed queen of daytime talk shows and was the first African-American billionaire. She was born with a gift for public speaking and owns a large media company.

Stedman Graham
Oprah's long-term partner, Stedman is a tall, charismatic ex-basketball player. He is also a successful public relations businessman and author.

Vernita Lee
Giving birth to Oprah at eighteen years old, Vernita was a single mother who struggled to bring up Oprah and her brother and sister.

Vernon Winfrey
Her father's strong discipline tamed Oprah during her difficult teenage years. He taught her self-discipline and helped guide her ambition. Vernon worked as a barber in Nashville, USA.

Hattie May Lee
Oprah's grandmother taught her to read at a very early age. She owned a farm in Mississippi, USA, where Oprah spent her childhood years.

Quincy Jones
This entertainment pioneer was pivotal in helping Oprah get her first acting role. He became a mentor and close friend.

CIVIL RIGHTS

Oprah Winfrey was born in 1954 in Kosciusko, Mississippi, USA, at a time when segregation existed across the South. These laws separated black citizens from whites and denied them basic civil liberties. It was tough for poor African-Americans to improve their lives. But things were changing.

HUMAN BONDAGE
Many slaves were bought by Southern plantation owners.

THE FIGHT FOR RIGHTS

The first Africans had arrived in America as slaves. They had very few rights and were often abused. In 1865, following the American Civil War, slavery was abolished and the former slaves were given new powers. Despite these changes, the laws in the South meant that African-Americans were still victims of racism.

Oprah Winfrey was less than a year old when, in 1955, a woman named Rosa Parks refused to give up her seat on a bus to a white man, as she was required to do by law. Parks's defiance against the humiliating segregation laws jump-started the battle to improve conditions for African-Americans. Parks, and preacher Martin Luther King, led the way to social change.

POOR SERVICE
A young person drinks from a segregated drinking fountain in Halifax, North Carolina, USA, in 1938. Everything was separated under segregation.

MARTIN LUTHER KING
Famous for his 'I Have a Dream' speech, Martin Luther King was a passionate campaigner for human rights. During the 1960s he helped African-Americans to gain equal access to public facilities, education and voting.

FREE AT LAST
When King was assassinated, Oprah was a troubled fourteen-year-old living in Milwaukee, USA. Although she was unaware of it at the time, King's legacy would enable Oprah to build her future career.

King's belief in judging people by their actions, not by their skin colour, helped change the laws which had prevented talented African-Americans from achieving their dreams.

CIVIL RIGHTS HEROINES
Harriet Tubman and Rosa Parks were inspirational figures for Oprah. Both fought for social justice despite being threatened with strict punishments. Rosa Parks was arrested for refusing to let a white man sit in her bus seat. Harriet Tubman was a slave who escaped from her owners to Philadelphia, USA. She was fearless in her determination to lead blacks out of slavery. Despite the dangers involved, including threats to her life, Tubman continued her fight.

HARRIET TUBMAN
Strong characters like Harriet Tubman, who guided slaves to freedom during the 1880s, were beacons that lit the way for black women of the future.

IT'S SHOWTIME!

In 1963, the power of television helped Martin Luther King to spread his message of peace across America. Although television had been around for 40 years, it only became popular in the 1950s.

STAYING TUNED
Since the 1950s, television has been a major source of entertainment.

MAKING THE AIRWAVES

During the first half of the 1950s, ownership of televisions in the United States skyrocketed. The first television networks were part of the larger radio networks, and many early television programmes were created from popular radio shows.

As the established U.S. television networks – ABC, CBS and NBC – gained money from advertising, they invested in television studios and new talent, developing shows specifically for the small screen.

SERIOUS BUSINESS
Before The Today Show, *TV interviews were often a solemn business involving national leaders on issues of state. A typical show was NBC's weekly* Meet the Press.

PRIME TIME

In 1952, NBC launched the first, and what would become the longest-running, early-morning network show. It was called *The Today Show* and combined serious news stories with lighter features. Its hosts were ex-athlete Dave Garroway and a chimpanzee named J. Fred Muggs.

In 1954, NBC launched *The Tonight Show*, featuring comedian Steve Allen. The success of *The Today Show* and *The Tonight Show*, with their mixture of news, topical discussion and live entertainment would lead to the development of a popular new daytime format – the TV talk show.

As Simple as ABC

ABC, the American Broadcasting Company, has been one of the most influential networks in changing the television landscape in the USA. It was the first to hire a woman, Barbara Walters, from NBC, as its evening anchor. With a contract worth $1,000,000 (£556,000) in 1976, Walters became the most celebrated woman in television news. Producing an acclaimed series of interview programmes, she served as an inspiring figure to Oprah Winfrey.

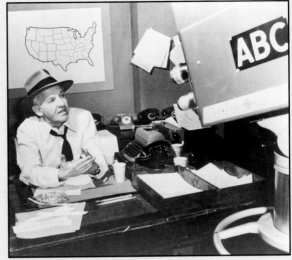

Innovator
ABC made its mark in television history with its bold daytime and primetime programming.

Let's Talk

Radio journalist Phil Donahue was the first person to establish 'talk television'. His daytime show, *Donahue*, was an extension of the live radio call-in shows of the 1960s. His TV show featured audience members talking about the social issues that affected their lives. Very quickly, it became a runaway success.

Oprah's Early Life

Oprah Gail Winfrey was born on 29 January, 1954, to a poor, young woman named Vernita Lee. Several people took care of Oprah when she was a child, including her grandmother, and then her father, Vernon Winfrey, who was a barber and former U.S. Navy sailor.

Mis-Named
Oprah was actually named 'Orpah' on her birth certificate. It has been mispronounced since as 'Oprah'.

OPRAH WINFREY
THE LIFE OF A MEDIA SUPERSTAR

22 SEPTEMBER, 2002...

...AND WELCOME BACK TO THE 54TH ANNUAL EMMY AWARDS, AS ACTOR TOM HANKS HANDS OVER THE FIRST-EVER BOB HOPE HUMANITARIAN AWARD TO REIGNING TALK SHOW QUEEN OPRAH WINFREY.

OPRAH IS AMERICA'S FIRST AFRICAN-AMERICAN BILLIONAIRE. IN RECENT YEARS, SHE HAS USED HER SHOW TO DRAW ATTENTION TO THE ISSUES SHE HOLDS DEAR.

THERE REALLY IS NOTHING MORE IMPORTANT TO ME THAN STRIVING TO BE A GOOD HUMAN BEING.

9

AFTER EIGHTEEN MONTHS...

OPRAH, I'M SORRY, BUT I CAN'T AFFORD TO TAKE CARE OF BOTH YOU AND PATRICIA.

LATER...

YOUR FATHER HAS AGREED THAT YOU SHOULD LIVE WITH HIM.

TWO WEEKS LATER, IN NASHVILLE, TENNESSEE, OPRAH WAS MET BY VERNON WINFREY AND HIS WIFE, ZELMA.

OPRAH, YOU'VE GROWN SO **BIG**!

SHE'S PRETTY, TOO!

AND VERY CLEVER ACCORDING TO VERNITA.

IN MILWAUKEE, OPRAH HAD GONE STRAIGHT FROM FIRST TO THIRD GRADE.

16

THE WINFREYS ENROLLED OPRAH INTO THE EAST WHARTON ELEMENTARY SCHOOL, WHERE SHE MADE A BIG IMPRESSION.

WELL, I CONFESS, NOBODY HAS EVER READ THE MORNING DEVOTIONS SO WELL. OPRAH, WHERE DID YOU LEARN TO SPEAK SO BEAUTIFULLY?

I LEARNED IN CHURCH, MISS DUNCAN!

AT BREAK...

HEY, PREACHER! ARE YOU STILL GOING TO JOIN THE MINISTRY?

ACTUALLY, I'VE DECIDED TO BE A MISSIONARY!

OPRAH IGNORED THEIR TEASING. IT WAS HER AMBITION, AFTER GRADUATING, TO USE THE POWER OF THE CHURCH TO HELP THE NEEDY. WHEN SHE TURNED NINE, HOWEVER...

IT'S FROM YOUR MOTHER.

...VERNITA WAS PREGNANT AND PLANNING TO GET MARRIED. SHE WANTED OPRAH HOME TO COMPLETE HER FAMILY.

17

IF YOU WERE A C STUDENT YOU COULD, BUT YOU ARE AN **A** STUDENT, SO **A'S** ARE WHAT WE EXPECT IN THIS HOUSE!

IN ADDITION TO TRYING HARD AT SCHOOL, OPRAH WAS REQUIRED TO READ A NEW BOOK EVERY TWO WEEKS AND SUBMIT A REPORT ON IT TO HER FATHER. OPRAH WORKED HARD.

SHE SOON ROSE TO THE TOP OF HER CLASS AT EAST NASHVILLE HIGH. IN THE TWELFTH GRADE, SHE WAS ONE OF TWO STUDENTS SELECTED FROM EACH STATE TO GO TO A WHITE HOUSE CONFERENCE ON YOUTH. THIS LED TO AN INTERVIEW WITH RADIO STATION WVOL IN NASHVILLE.

OPRAH AND GAIL KING, AN ASSISTANT AT WJZ-TV, HAD BECOME GOOD FRIENDS.

GAIL, NOTHING CAN MATCH THE PLEASURES OF A WELL-BAKED POTATO!

LET ME GET THIS STRAIGHT. YOU HAVEN'T BEEN FIRED, JUST MOVED TO A MORNING TALK SHOW?

YES, THE SHOW IS ONLY FIVE MINUTES LONG. FIVE MINUTES AT FIVE-THIRTY IN THE MORNING!

SO, HOW ARE YOU GOING TO APPROACH IT?

AS THE HOST OF 'PEOPLE ARE TALKING', I INTEND TO MODEL MYSELF ON PHIL DONAHUE.* I'M GOING TO BE THE FEMALE DONAHUE!

*U.S. MEDIA LEGEND PHIL DONAHUE HAD REVOLUTIONISED THE TV TALK SHOW FORMAT BY GETTING A LIVE AUDIENCE DIRECTLY INVOLVED IN THE DISCUSSION OF SERIOUS ISSUES.

AFTER HER FIRST DAY TAPING THE NEW SHOW, OPRAH WAS OVERJOYED.

YES! THAT WAS AS EASY AS BREATHING!

OPRAH WAS A NATURAL IN THE TALK SHOW FORMAT. BY THE EARLY 1980S, SHE BEGAN ATTRACTING THE ATTENTION OF LARGER TV NETWORKS, LIKE WLS-TV. IN 1983...

MR SWANSON, I'M REALLY HAPPY TO WORK FOR YOU AT WLS HERE IN CHICAGO, HOWEVER, YOU MUST HAVE SOME CONCERNS. AFTER ALL, I **AM** AFRICAN-AMERICAN!*

*CHICAGO WAS NOT KNOWN FOR ITS RACIAL TOLERANCE AT THIS TIME.

SO?

DENNIS SWANSON, BOSS OF WLS-TV, WANTED OPRAH TO TAKE OVER AS THE HOST OF A FAILING TALK SHOW CALLED 'AM CHICAGO'.

AND THERE'S MY SIZE. I'M A LITTLE **HEAVY** AT THE MOMENT.

UNHAPPY WITH HER PAYMENT FROM WLS, OPRAH WENT TO SEE TOP ENTERTAINMENT LAWYER JEFFREY JACOBS.

SO, THEY CALL YOU THE PIRANHA! THAT'S WHAT I NEED, A PIRANHA!

JACOBS GOT A BETTER DEAL FOR OPRAH. LATER, HE BECAME HER TRUSTED ADVISER.

IN HER SPARE TIME, OPRAH READ PASSIONATELY AND HAD FURTHER AMBITIONS.

The Color Pur

WHAT I WOULDN'T GIVE TO PLAY THE ROLE OF SOFIA!

THE NOVEL 'THE COLOR PURPLE' WAS BEING DEVELOPED INTO A FILM.

IN 1984, THE SINGER QUINCY JONES, CO-PRODUCER OF 'THE COLOR PURPLE' WITH DIRECTOR STEVEN SPIELBERG, HAPPENED TO BE STAYING IN CHICAGO WHEN...

STEVEN? STEVEN! IT'S QUINCY, PUT THE CASTING SESSIONS ON HOLD...

33

DO YOU THINK YOU'LL EVER FIND HIM?

I DON'T KNOW...

...BUT I SURE HOPE SO.

OPRAH'S PERFORMANCE IN 'THE COLOR PURPLE' EARNED HER AN OSCAR NOMINATION.

MEANWHILE, 'AM CHICAGO' WAS RE-NAMED 'THE OPRAH WINFREY SHOW'. IT WAS SOLD TO STATIONS ACROSS AMERICA. THEN, IN MAY 1986...

OPRAH, WOULD YOU CONSIDER GOING ON A DATE WITH ME?

STEDMAN GRAHAM WAS AN EX-BASKETBALL STAR AND SUCCESSFUL BUSINESSMAN.

I THINK THAT WOULD JUST ABOUT DO IT!

'THE OPRAH WINFREY SHOW' WAS TO HAVE ITS NATIONAL DEBUT IN THE AUTUMN.

8 SEPTEMBER, 1986. OPRAH WROTE IN HER DIARY, AS SHE HAD DONE EVERY NIGHT SINCE SHE WAS FIFTEEN.

WE ARE TAPING THE FIRST-EVER 'OPRAH WINFREY SHOW' TOMORROW. I CAN'T HELP FEELING THAT I'M ON THE BRINK OF SOMETHING BIG.

IF SUCCESSFUL, OPRAH'S SALARY WOULD LEAP FROM $230,000 (£157,000) PER YEAR TO OVER $30 MILLION (£20 MILLION). BUT MONEY WASN'T HER MOST PRESSING CONCERN.

IS THIS JUST ENTERTAINMENT OR SOMETHING MORE IMPORTANT? MAYBE BROADCASTING TO THE NATION WILL HELP ME FIND OUT.

37

HELLO, AND WELCOME TO THE SHOW. TODAY, OUR TOPIC IS HOW TO FIND THE RIGHT PERSON TO SPEND YOUR LIFE WITH. IN THE STUDIO, WE HAVE...

IN THE CROWDED TALK SHOW FIELD, 'THE OPRAH WINFREY SHOW' PROVED TO BE A RUNAWAY SUCCESS. OVERNIGHT, OPRAH BECAME A MULTI-MILLIONAIRE. USING HER RICHES, SHE PURCHASED A STUDIO FACILITY AND TOOK OVER THE PRODUCTION OF HER SHOW.

THANK YOU FOR WATCHING. WE'LL SEE YOU AGAIN TOMORROW WHEN WE WILL BE FEATURING INCREDIBLE STORIES OF FRIENDSHIP.

WITHIN A MONTH, OPRAH HAD PUT MOST OF THE WEIGHT BACK ON. WHEN SHE ACCEPTED HER 1993 DAYTIME EMMY SHE WAS 226 LB (103 KG), HER HEAVIEST WEIGHT EVER.

I AM NOT HAPPY BEING THIS HEAVY.

IN 1994, WITH THE HELP OF A PERSONAL TRAINER AND DIETICIAN, OPRAH FINALLY CONQUERED HER WEIGHT PROBLEM.

IN 1995, AFTER INTENSIVE TRAINING, SHE COMPLETED THE MARINE CORPS MARATHON.

IN 1996, OPRAH'S LOVE OF LITERATURE LED HER TO START HER OWN BOOK CLUB. HER INFLUENCE WAS SO POWERFUL THAT THE BOOKS SHE RECOMMENDED BECAME BESTSELLERS OVERNIGHT.

41

THAT SAME YEAR, OPRAH GAVE THE GRADUATION SPEECH TO THE STUDENTS OF WELLESLEY COLLEGE, IN THE STATE OF MASSACHUSETTS.

THERE'S ONE FINAL THING I WANT TO SHARE WITH YOU.

CREATE THE HIGHEST, GRANDEST VISION POSSIBLE FOR YOUR LIFE BECAUSE YOU BECOME WHAT YOU BELIEVE.

EVEN WHEN I WAS FOUR YEARS OLD, BAREFOOT ON A FARM IN SEGREGATED MISSISSIPPI, I KNEW THAT MY LIFE COULD BE BETTER. SO DON'T BE AFRAID TO DREAM BIG!

HONOURED FOR HER GOOD WORK OVER THE YEARS, OPRAH WINFREY CONTINUES TO BE REGARDED IN THE USA AS TALK TELEVISION'S MOST INFLUENTIAL VOICE.

THE END

PUBLIC SERVICE

Oprah's enormous wealth and influence have come from the popularity of her talk show. There have been many other successful talk show hosts, but nobody like Oprah. What's her secret?

MAKING THE CONNECTION

At times, Oprah has described her show as being a non-religious sermon for ordinary people. It offers advice on familiar, everyday problems, as well as hope and guidance in difficult times.

Oprah's empathy – the ability to connect with another person's feelings – has won her the hearts of millions of viewers. Her clear and genuine understanding of an individual's situation forges a link between Oprah and the audience, as well as the guests on the show itself.

Unafraid to explore her own failings under the glare of the TV spotlight, Oprah's openness and honesty have inspired great trust in her viewers. They feel close to her, taking her advice and believing her judgement.

BUSINESS SAVVY

Oprah's prosperity has been secured through clever business decisions. When she first started building her business empire, she vowed to hire people who were smarter than herself. Oprah hires the brightest and best, but her real genius has been to reward hard work generously, breeding a fierce loyalty among her staff. She also runs a tight ship, signing every outgoing cheque personally to keep track of expenses.

In the new millennium Oprah has successfully expanded her business empire to include the Internet, cable TV, and publishing. She owns a television station, a magazine called O, and a Web site that provides lifestyle advice.

OPENING THE DOOR

From her own life experience, Oprah has said she believes education is the key to helping people to improve their lives. Among the many causes that Oprah supports through her charitable work, education is a priority. She funds scholarships for individuals who have the merit but lack the finance to go to college, as well as programmes to build schools.

THE NATION'S CONSCIENCE

Oprah has become an important public figure in America during times of crisis. Following the 11 September, 2001, terrorist attacks, she offered emotional comfort to a shocked nation. In the aftermath of Hurricane Katrina, Oprah acted as an unofficial spokesperson for the victims, questioning the government, rallying help, and raising issues of racial divisions in America.

Oprah talks periodically about her retirement. However, in 2005, she extended her contract with ABC television, confirming that she will continue to present *The Oprah Winfrey Show* until at least 2011.

LEADERSHIP TRAINING

In 2002, Oprah Winfrey and former South African president Nelson Mandela launched the $10 million (£6 million) Leadership Academy for Girls in South Africa. Mandela, a keen Oprah fan, has hailed her as a 'hero' and a 'queen' for her charitable work.

GLOSSARY

abolish To get rid of something forever.

acclaimed Celebrated by many people.

adviser A person who gives guidance.

airwaves The radio and TV waves used for broadcasting programmes.

anchor A television news presenter in the USA.

assassination The killing of a person, often secretly, and always planned in advance. People are often assassinated for political reasons.

beacon A source of inspiration.

campaigner A person who carries out an action, or a set of actions, for a particular cause. He or she may act alone or as part of a group.

civil right A power or privilege, such as a personal freedom that everyone is entitled to under acts of Congress and the 13th and 14th Amendments to the U.S. Constitution.

civil war A war where divisions within a group fight each other. The American Civil War lasted from 1861 to 1865.

condominium A kind of apartment or purpose-built flat.

conference A formal meeting of two or more people to discuss a particular subject or concern.

defiance A strong refusal to give up an object, idea or point of view.

devastate To destroy.

exploit Use of an individual or object for one's personal gain.

gratitude To show appreciation for something.

guardian A caregiver who is responsible for a child's welfare in place of the child's parent.

humanitarian Describes an action carried out to help a particular group of people.

humiliation Making fun of a person to cause embarrassment, hurt, or upset, destroying that person's self-respect and dignity.

intimidate To instill fear based on the strength of one's character.

judgement A strong opinion.

juvenile hall A young people's prison.

legacy Something handed down from a person of an older generation.

ministry A group of people who guide a religion.

piranha A small fish with very sharp teeth.

proclaim To announce something.

represent To appear on behalf of another individual or organization.

runaway success Something that has turned out extremely well.

segregation Separation of the races.

sponsor To give money to a programme, often in return for advertising.

tight ship A strictly controlled group or organization.

tolerance Putting up with something without necessarily enjoying it.

unique The only one; a one-off.

welfare A type of care that ensures the best outcome for someone.

FURTHER READING

Brooks, Philip. *Oprah Winfrey; A Voice for the People.*
London, Franklin Watts, 2000.

Hudak, Heather C. *Oprah Winfrey* (Great African American Women).
New York, NY: Weigl Publishers, 2005.

Krohn, Katherine E. *Oprah Winfrey* (Just the Facts Biographies).
Minneapolis, MN: Lerner Publications Company, 2004.

Lowe, Janet. *Oprah Winfrey Speaks: Insight from the World's Most
Influential Voice.* New York, NY: John Wiley & Sons, Inc., 1998.

Nicholson, Lois P. *Oprah Winfrey* (Black Americans of Achievement).
New York, NY: Chelsea House Publications, 1994.

Stone, Tanya Lee. *Oprah Winfrey: Success with an Open Heart.*
Brookfield, CT: Millbrook Press, 2001.

Weil, Anne. *Oprah Winfrey Queen of Daytime TV* (Business Whizzes).
Parsippany, NJ: Crestwood House, 1998.

Westen, Robin. *Oprah Winfrey: "I Don't Believe in Failure"* (African
American Biography). Berkeley Heights, NJ: Enslow Publishers, 2005.

Wooten, Sara McIntosh. *Oprah Winfrey: Talk Show Legend* (African
American Biographies). Berkeley Heights, NJ: Enslow Publishers, 1999.

INDEX